INSIDE

STRIP STORIES

ALSO INSIDE

£7.99

▶▶▶ *Hey, Marvelites! Want to know all about the Falcon? Read on to discover all his super-powered secrets!*

PAST CRIMES!

He may be a good guy these days, but Sam Wilson wasn't always a high-flying hero. As a younger man he worked for a smuggling racket in the Caribbean, until the day his plane crashed on a remote island.

ISLAND LIFE!

Stranded on the island, Sam spent his time training his pet hunting falcon Redwing. Eventually, Sam was rescued when Captain America came to the island in pursuit of the evil super villain the Red Skull.

A NEW BEGINNING!

After witnessing Captain America in action, Sam was so impressed he renounced his criminal ways and asked Cap if he could join him. He agreed and the two returned to America where Sam became Cap's new partner, the Falcon.

INSIDE THE FALCON'S WINGS

Electric positioning arm for turbine / fan arms.

Wing to arm brace.

Wings fitted with solar cells which constantly charge the batteries.

Power cells

Uni-directional arm joints

Micro-turbine air jets.

Spring tensioned arm and rib supports.

FALCON FACT:

Whilst in flight the Falcon can reach a top speed of 140 miles per hour.

POWER RANKING:

STRENGTH: 9
SPEED: 14
INTELLIGENCE: 12
AGILITY: 11
POWERS: 9

FALCON FACT:
Captain America has trained the Falcon to be an expert martial artist.

THE FALCON

FALCON FACT:
Sam has an empathic link with his pet Falcon Redwing and can also psychically 'see' through the eyes of other nearby birds.

NAME: Sam Wilson
HEIGHT: 6' 2"
WEIGHT: 240 LBS
EQUIPMENT: Jet-propelled flying harness.
POWERS / ABILITIES: Expert at hand-to-hand combat, plus the power to psychically communicate with birds.

"INITIAL INSERTION WILL BE AT REFERENCE POINT DELTA-SEVEN-ECHO, TWO KLIKS NORTH OF THE HUNGARIAN BORDER.

SCRIPT: FERG HANDLEY
PENCILS: IAN RICHARDSON
INKS: LEE TOWNSEND
COLOURS: DIGIKORE
LETTERING: TIM WARRAN-SMITH
STRIP EDITOR: ED HAMMOND

"AFTER THAT, IT'S A CASE OF FLYING FAST AND LOW TO AVOID THE RADAR NET..."

"...AND ONCE INSIDE LATVERIAN AIRSPACE, YOU WILL MAINTAIN A BEARING OF ONE-NINER-FIVE DEGREES..."

...WHICH WILL TAKE YOU STRAIGHT TO CASTLE DOOM

THEN I JUST KNOCK ON THE DOOR, RIGHT?

HARDLY, FALCON. WE'RE SUPPLYING YOU WITH THIS *E.M.P.* SPIKE...

*ELECTRO-MAGNETIC PULSE. - ELECTRICAL ED.

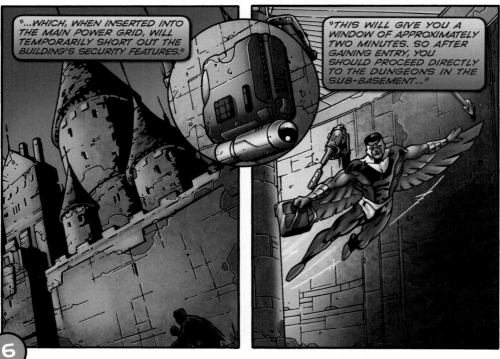

"...WHICH, WHEN INSERTED INTO THE MAIN POWER GRID, WILL TEMPORARILY SHORT OUT THE BUILDING'S SECURITY FEATURES."

"THIS WILL GIVE YOU A WINDOW OF APPROXIMATELY TWO MINUTES. SO AFTER GAINING ENTRY, YOU SHOULD PROCEED DIRECTLY TO THE DUNGEONS IN THE SUB-BASEMENT..."

"...AND CRACK OPEN THE ALPHA-LEVEL HOLDING CELL."

KA BOOM

SAM? IS THAT *YOU?*

SURE IS, CAP. BUT MAN, LOOK AT THE STATE OF YOU!

I'LL LIVE, SAM... DOOM'S NOT THE FIRST TWO-BIT TYRANT TO BEAT ON ME, AND I DOUBT HE'LL BE THE LAST.

CLICK

OKAY, NOW STRAP ON THIS JET PACK. THE AUTO-PILOT'S KEYED INTO MY HARNESS, SO IT'LL REPLICATE MY *EXACT* FLIGHT PATH.

BETTER HURRY THOUGH, 'COS THE AUXILIARY GENERATORS ARE ABOUT TO KICK IN...

"...AND YOU KNOW WHAT DOOM'S SECURITY SYSTEMS ARE LIKE."

ZZZT!

BUDDA BUDDA BUDDA

FWAAAASH

GERONIMO!!! MAN, I ALWAYS WANTED TO SAY THAT!

...NGH...

YOU OKAY, SAM?

BEEN BETTER, CAP. AND THE WINGS ARE TOTALLED, SO IT LOOKS LIKE WE'RE *WALKING* OUT OF HERE- -

UNLIKELY, AMERICAN.

DOOM! OR ONE OF HIS DOOMBOTS, ANYWAY.

NO, IT IS I.

AND NOW, PREPARE TO PAY THE ULTIMATE PRICE FOR THIS VIOLATION OF MY COUNTRY'S SOVEREIGNTY.

NO WAY, TIN MAN. WE MUST BE IN HUNGARY BY NOW, WHICH MEANS - -

ENOUGH. IT IS TWO HUNDRED METERS TO THE FRONTIER, WHICH MEANS I STILL HAVE JURISDICTION HERE.

SUIT YOURSELF, DOOM! IF IT'S A *FIGHT* YOU WANT- -

A FIGHT? HARDLY.

VA-WOOOMPH

UNNNGH!

...AND IF YOU WANT PROOF, JUST TAKE A LOOK AT THE WOUND POINT.

WHOA, YOU'RE RIGHT... AIN'T NOTHING BUT METAL AND CIRCUITS IN THERE.

YOU WON'T GET AWAY WITH THIS! I AM *DOOM*, AND — —

AND *NOTHING*. WE'RE LEAVING NOW, AND JUDGING BY THE STATE OF YOUR ARMOUR...

...THERE'S NOT A LOT YOU CAN DO TO STOP US.

DARNED STRAIGHT.

SO, YOU WANT TO TELL ME WHAT'S GOING ON HERE, CAP?

SURE, SAM. THE ANDROID'S AN ADVANCED *LIFE DECOY MODEL*, PART OF A NEW S.H.I.E.L.D. INITIATIVE...

A GLITCH? WELL THAT EXPLAINS WHY IT CALLED ME *'RICK'* BACK THERE.

"...AND IN ORDER TO IMPROVE ITS FIGHTING SKILLS, THE BOFFINS DECIDED TO PROGRAMME IT WITH SIMULATIONS OF MY OLD MISSIONS ..."

...INCLUDING A COVERT OP TO DESTROY A MILITARY SATELLITE, WHICH HAD CRASHED IN LATVERIAN TERRITORY.

PROBLEM WAS, THE ANDROID MUST'VE HAD A GLITCH IN ITS SYSTEM...

PROBABLY. ANYHOW...

ALTERED VISION!

Greetings readers. I am the Vision. My optical sensors have detected that there are ten differences between these two pictures. Test your own powers of perception and see if you can spot them all!

Answers: 1 - Flag in Nick Fury's gun. 2 - Giant Girl's hair. 3 - Rabbit in Iron Man's hand. 4 - Top Hat in Man's hand. 5 - Heart on Cap's shield. 6 - Cake in Venom's hands. 7 - Vision is wearing a hat. 8 - Person missing behind Giant Girl. 9 - Spaceman in background. 10 - Head changed from Red to blue.

MARVEL ▶▶▶
MASTERPIECE!

The unstoppable JUGGERNAUT is on the rampage and it's up to the X-Men to halt him in his tracks! Grab your pens and help them take him down in style by adding some colour to this scene!

COLOUR GUIDE ▶▶▶

CLAYTON FARM -- PRAIRIE TOWN, ARKANSAS.

I PROMISE YOU WITH THESE MODIFICATIONS SHE'LL RUN BETTER THAN USAIN BOLT!

I DON'T KNOW ABOUT THAT, BRUCE...

THE INCREDIBLE HULK
OUT OF THE PAST

SCRIPT: JAMES PEATY
PENCILS & INKS: SIMON WILLIAMS COLOURS: DIGIKORE
LETTERING: WILL LUCAS
STRIP EDITOR: ED HAMMOND

...BUT WITH ALL THE OTHER CLEVER STUFF YOU'VE BEEN ABLE TO DO THESE LAST MONTHS YOU'VE REALLY HELPED THIS FARM STAY AFLOAT.

JUST DOING WHAT ANY GOOD EMPLOYEE WOULD DO, BILL.

KRUNCHK

DON'T BE A KIDDER.

I MAY NOT BE A MAN OF THE WORLD...

GOOD BOY!

...BUT WHATEVER IT WAS YOU DID BEFORE YOU PITCHED UP HERE, IT SURE AS HECK WASN'T MILKING COWS AND BAILING HAY!

I REALLY DON'T LIKE TALKING ABOUT ALL THA--

DRINKS ARE READY!

THANKS, HONEY.

THAT REALLY HITS THE SPOT, MRS CLAYTON.

OH, DON'T BE SILLY...

...AFTER ALL THE GOOD FORTUNE YOU'VE BROUGHT TO THIS FARM, IT'S THE LEAST YOU DESERVE.

THAT'S VERY KIND OF YOU, MA'AM.

BUT LETS LEAVE IT AWHILE BEFORE DECIDING WHETHER I'VE BROUGHT ANYTHING GOOD HERE OR NO --

NARGH!

KZZZTTZ

15

THE REPAIR COSTS TO YOUR FARM AND THE COMPENSATION FOR YOUR INCONVENIENCE WILL BE COVERED DIRECTLY BY SHIELD, MR CLAYTON.

THAT'S AWFUL KIND OF YOU, SIR.

HOWEVER, SHIELD *DOES* EXPECT THE UTMOST *DISCRETION* IN RETURN FOR OUR *GENEROSITY*.

OF COURSE, AGENT DUGAN...

EVERYTHING OK?

I GUESS SO.

RATHER THAN GETTING BRAINWASHED TO KEEP OUR MOUTHS SHUT THIS TIME WE'RE GETTING *PAID*.

LOOKS LIKE BRUCE REALLY DID BRING GOOD FORTUNE AFTER ALL.

DID YOU TELL THEM WHERE THE HULK WAS HEADED?

I TOLD THEM HE WENT NORTH.

BUT DAD...

...YOU SAID TO ME HE WENT SOUTH?

DID I?

YEAH.

DARN...

...LOOKS LIKE BRUCE MIGHT'VE FINALLY GOTTEN A SLICE OF HIS OWN GOOD FORTUNE.

WELL, IN THAT CASE I HOPE HE MAKES GOOD USE OF IT...

"...COS LORD KNOWS HE NEEDS IT!"

THE END.

21

Hulk's troubles aren't over yet! See if you can help him stay one step ahead of Hydra by completing these missions!

1 SEND IN THE CLONES!

⊗ MISSION I

Hydra have created the ultimate evil team to stop the Hulk by cloning four heroes! Can you tell which hero each of these chaotic copycats are based on?

1

C ☐☐☐☐☐☐
A ☐☐☐☐☐☐☐

2

I ☐☐☐☐
M ☐☐☐

3

H ☐☐☐☐☐☐

4

T ☐☐☐

HYDRA

A group of hi-tech super-terrorists who spread chaos and confusion in a bid to overthrow governments and achieve total global domination!

MADAME HYDRA

Leader of the U.S. division of HYDRA. She is a highly trained warrior and an expert battlefield tactician.

"Hail HYDRA! Immortal HYDRA! We will never be destroyed! Cut off a limb and two more shall take its place!"

2 CRACK THE CODE!

⊗ MISSION 2

Madame Hydra has sent a secret code to all her troops telling them which weapon to use against the Hulk. Using the code below, see if you can work out what it says?

TRANSLATION CODE:

ﾃﾞ=A ｼﾞ=B ･ﾂﾞ=C ﾆﾞ=D ｱ=E ﾉﾞ=F
ｷﾞ=G ﾀﾞ=H ｲ=I ﾚﾞ=J ｹﾞ=K ﾍﾞ=L
ﾎﾞ=M ﾂﾞ=N ｵﾞ=O ﾒﾞ=P ﾄﾞ=Q ﾘﾞ=R
ｼﾞ=S ﾃﾞ=T ｳﾞ=U ﾜﾞ=V ｳﾞ=W ﾑﾞ=X
ﾆﾞ=Y ﾀﾞ=Z

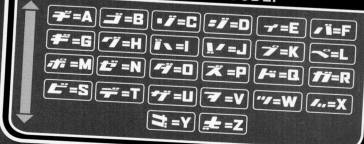

☐☐☐☐☐   ☐☐☐☐☐☐☐

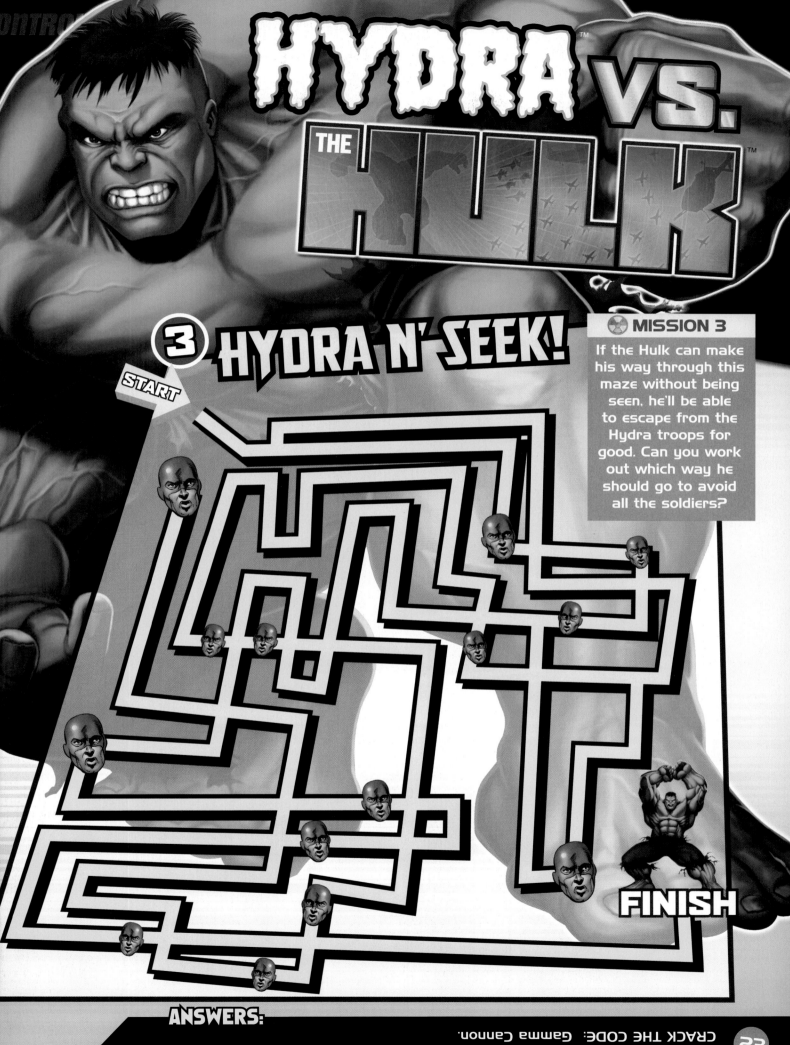

HYDRA vs. THE HULK

③ HYDRA N' SEEK!

START

⊗ **MISSION 3**

If the Hulk can make his way through this maze without being seen, he'll be able to escape from the Hydra troops for good. Can you work out which way he should go to avoid all the soldiers?

FINISH

ANSWERS:

SEND IN THE CLONES: 1 - Captain America, 2 - Iron Man, 3 - Hawkeye, 4 - Thor.
CRACK THE CODE: Gamma Cannon.

NAME: Clint Barton
HEIGHT: 6' 3"
WEIGHT: 230 LBS
POWERS | ABILITIES:
Expert archer with near-perfect accuracy, plus almost superhuman eye-sight and reflexes.

With an expert eye and bow skills that put Robin Hood to shame, Hawkeye is one hero who never fails to hit the target! Read on to find out all about him!

HAWKEYE FACT:
He has the same level of agility as an olympic level athlete.

You'd think a bow wouldn't be much good in a scrap with Super Villains like Dr Doom, but Hawkeye has an arsenal of special trick arrows in his quiver to give him the edge in battle. Below are just a few of his cool custom arrows!

WEBBING

ACID BOMB

SMOKE SCREEN

GRAPPLING HOOK

EXPLOSIVE TIPPED

Hawkeye is the world's greatest archer and regularly trains up to 6 hours every day to keep his bowskills at their peak.

THE ORIGINS OF... HAWKEYE™

RAISED IN A TRAVELLING CIRCUS, CLINT BARTON HAD BEEN TAUGHT FROM AN EARLY AGE TO BE AN EXPERT BOWMAN.

UNDER THE STAGE NAME OF HAWKEYE THE MARKSMAN HE WOWED CROWDS WITH HIS AMAZING SKILLS.

GROWING BORED OF HIS LIFE IN THE CIRCUS, HE DECIDED TO USE HIS SKILLS TO FIGHT CRIME.

BUT ON HIS FIRST MISSION HE WAS STOPPED BY IRON MAN, WHO MISTOOK HIM FOR A CRIMINAL.

THIS IS THE LAST JEWELLERY SHOP YOU KNOCK OVER, MISTER!

BACK OFF, SHELL HEAD. I'M INNOCENT!

ON THE RUN FROM THE LAW, HAWKEYE JOINED UP WITH THE RUSSIAN SPY THE BLACK WIDOW AND TURNED TO A LIFE OF CRIME.

POWER RANKING:

STRENGTH:	9
SPEED:	7
INTELLIGENCE:	9
AGILITY:	10
POWERS:	12

HAWKEYE FACT:
Each of his arrows has a small notch in the end so he can tell by touch what type of arrows he's pulling out of his quiver.

HAWKEYE FACT:
Hawkeye has exceptional hand-to-hand combat skills taught to him by Captain America.

HAWKEYE

BUT WHEN THE BLACK WIDOW WAS NEARLY ASSASSINATED, HAWKEYE DECIDED TO GIVE UP ON HIS UNLAWFUL LIFE AND TRY ONCE AGAIN TO BE A HERO.

HE APPROACHED THE AVENGERS AND BEGGED THEM TO LET HIM JOIN THE TEAM.

WHAT DO YOU SAY, TIN-BRITCHES? AM I IN?

ALRIGHT, BARTON. YOU DESERVE THE CHANCE TO PROVE YOU'VE CHANGED.

I'LL SPONSOR YOU FOR MEMBERSHIP.

WITH HIS CRIMINAL WAYS BEHIND HIM, HAWKEYE NOW FIGHTS SIDE-BY-SIDE WITH SOME OF THE WORLD'S GREATEST HEROES AS A MEMBER OF THE AVENGERS!

25

STORY: SCOTT GRAY PENCILS: CARLOS GOMEZ INKS: GARY ERSKINE COLOURS: JOHN CHARLES LETTERING: TIM WARRAN-SMITH EDITOR: ED HAMMOND

AS I TAKE AIM, TIME SEEMS TO FREEZE... AND I FEEL OTHERS AROUND ME.
OTHER WARRIORS... CHAMPIONS... HEROES. THEY ALL USED THE BOW IN THE PAST...
AND NOW IT'S MY TURN.
THEN TIME STARTS UP AGAIN...
TWANG
AND I LET HER RIP!
NO!!! THE STAR --
K-KREESH
THE STAR IS DESTROYED, XANDU -- WHICH MEANS YOU ARE NO LONGER PROTECTED FROM MY SKILLS!
I MAY ONLY HAVE ONE HAND IN PLAY...
...BUT I AM STILL THE SORCEROR SUPREME!
ARGH!

THE END.

MARVEL
MASTERPIECE!

Help our Marvel marksman, Hawkeye, find his weapon of choice. Complete this dot to dot then grab your pens and pencils to add a splash of colour!

COLOUR GUIDE:

A

B

C

D

START

27

26

2

28

3

25 24
19
23 18
7
4 6 22 20
5 8 21 14
9
12 13
31 C 11 10
32 C 15
16

29 30
35 33 C
34 A
C 49
48 51 50
52 47
53 45 46
54 44 42
55 43
41

40

36

56 39

57

58
END 38

37

33

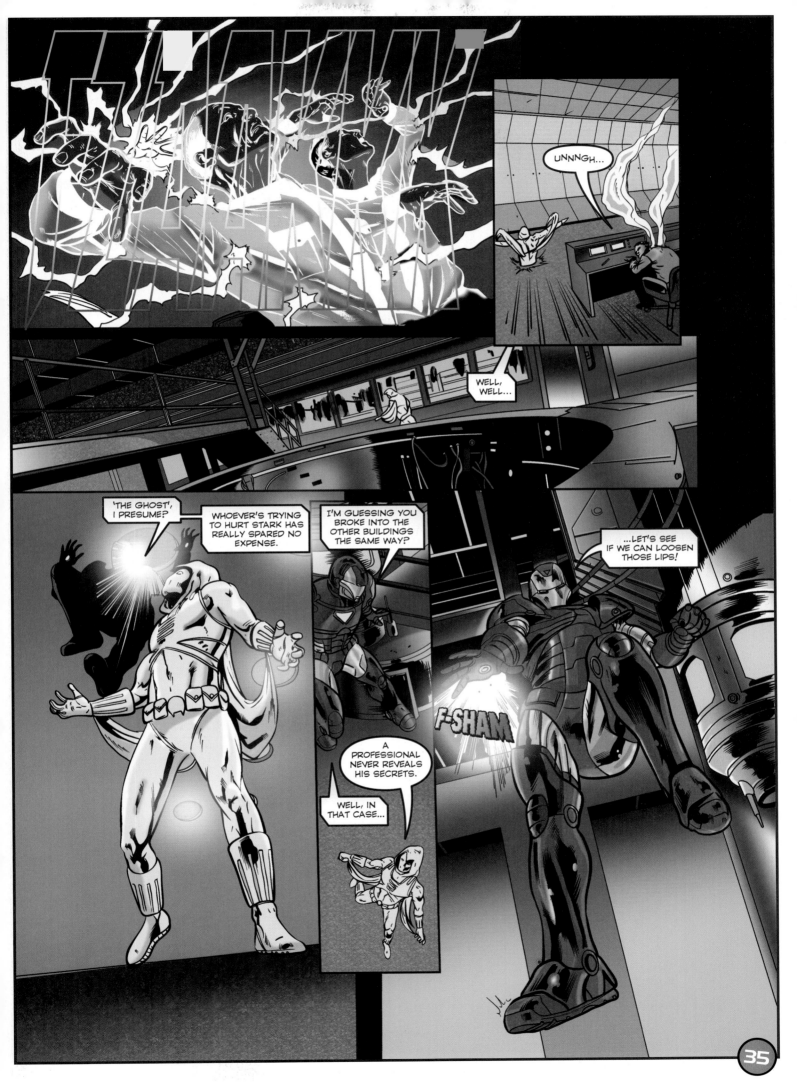

Hey Iron Maniacs! Think you could fly the Iron Man armour? Find out by solving these puzzles!

1 ENEMY ALERT!

MISSION 1

Tony Stark must constantly keep on his guard against a legion of Super Villains who are determined to destroy him. If you want to wear the Iron Man armour, you'll need to know about of all his nastiest foes!

Can you spot all their names in this word grid?

MANDARIN
TITANIUM MAN
GHOST
SPYMASTER
UNICORN
IRON MONGER
ULTRON
MODOK
VIBRO

		I	U	S	P	Y	M	A	S	T	E	R	
I	M	A	N	D	A	R	I	N	K	E	O	C
I	S	T	I	T	A	N	I	U	M	M	A	N	N
O	D	L	C	E	J	R	X	L	W	O	A	D	R
H	G	H	O	S	T	O	S	T	P	D	M	E	B
A	Y	E	R	I	V	I	B	R	O	O	S	N	P
P	O	N	N	S	Y	E	V	O	Y	K	W	W	E
	P	I	R	O	N	M	O	N	G	E	R	S	L
	T	W	S	T	J	J	E	L	I	U	R	

2 SYSTEM CHECK!

MISSION 2

In the heat of battle, Iron Man often has to reroute vital systems in his armour and perform emergency repairs, all whilst trying to avoid enemy fire. Test your skills by seeing if you can work out which circuit path will lead to the damaged chip!

A   B   C   D

CHIP

ANSWERS:

MARVEL STYLE!

SPIDER

STEP 1

First off, you need to draw the basic shapes that make up his body. Use a faint pencil to draw the head, shoulders, torso, arms and legs.

STEP 2

Once the basic blocks are drawn, you need to flesh out the body by filling in the arms and legs, and adding fingers.

STEP 3

Now you've got the basic shape, start adding details such as his muscles, eye mask and costume markings.

STEP 4

Next shade in the darker parts of his costume and add vertical lines for the web pattern on Spidey's suit.

MAN™

Check it out, guys! Do you want to be able to draw Spidey like one of our top artists? Just follow these 5 easy steps and you'll be a *Marvel Master* in no time!

STEP 5

Finish off by adding the web pattern to his suit, and then grab your pens and pencils and get colouring!

TRY IT YOURSELF!

THE END.

MARVEL MASTERPIECE!

Check it out, web heads! Grab your best pens and pencils and help Spidey take down Hydro-Man in style by colouring in this page!

COLOUR GUIDE

SPIDER STYLE!

Hey guys! All Super Heroes needs a change of wardrobe every once in a while and Spidey is no exception. Check out this round-up of some of the other cool costumes the webbed wonder has worn during his crime-fighting career!

CAPTAIN UNIVERSE!

Exposed to an alien energy called the Enigma Force, Spidey was temporarily transformed into a being known as Captain Universe. With a new cosmic powered costume, Spidey was amazed to find that his powers had been amplified to an almost god-like level!

POWERS/ABILITIES:

Enhanced speed, agility, strength and senses. He could also fire powerful blasts of cosmic energy

STEEL-SKIN SPIDEY!

When a heavily armed group of criminals called the New Enforcers starting causing trouble in New York, Peter Parker created a brand new armoured Spidey suit that was completely bullet-proof.

POWERS/ABILITIES:

Completely impervious to small arms and machine gun fire.

BLACK SUIT SPIDER-MAN!

Spidey acquired his black costume on an alien planet called Battleworld – but he soon ditched it when he discovered it was actually a living organism that was feeding off his body! Unfortunately for Spidey his discarded costume later bonded with Eddie Brock to form the twisted super villain Venom!

POWERS/ABILITIES:

Enhanced strength, able to change appearance at will and the ability to generate its own supply of webbing

THE IRON SPIDER!

Designed by Tony Stark, the robotic Iron Spider costume used advanced nano-technology to give Spidey state of the art powers and abilities! Coolest of all, the new costume featured three mechanical arms that Spidey could control with his mind.

POWERS/ABILITIES:

Armoured skin, flight, chameleon-like camouflage, enhanced vision, self-contained oxygen supply and three extra mechanical arms.

THE AMAZING BAG-MAN!

After Mr. Fantastic managed to remove his alien costume, Spidey was left with no clothes! Without a costume, the Web-Head had to use whatever was to hand to conceal his identity – and thus, the Amazing Bag-Man was born!

They are the world's first family of Super Heroes, a group of adventurers and explorers who have saved the world from peril countless times. Read on to find out all about the FANTASTIC FOUR!

HUMAN TORCH™

Real Name: Johnny Storm
Height: 5' 10"
Weight: 170 lbs
Powers and abilities:
Johnny has complete control over **fire** and can turn his entire body into **living flame.**

INVISIBLE WOMAN™

Real Name:
Sue Richards
Height: 5' 6"
Weight: 120 lbs
Powers and abilities:
Along with the ability to turn herself or others invisible, Sue can mentally project solid light force fields.

THE ORIGINS OF...

FANTASTIC FOUR™

REED RICHARDS WAS A BRILLIANT SCIENTIST WHO HAD SPENT YEARS DESIGNING THE WORLD'S FIRST INTERSTELLAR SPACECRAFT.

WITH THIS SHIP WE HAVE THE POWER TO TOUCH THE STARS AND EXPLORE SPACE FOR THE GOOD OF ALL MANKIND.

FOR ITS MAIDEN FLIGHT, REED ASKED HIS FIANCÉ SUE STORM, HER BROTHER JOHNNY AND HIS BEST FRIEND BEN GRIMM TO HELP HIM FLY THE SHIP.

BUT AS THE SHIP LEFT THE EARTH'S ATMOSPHERE IT WAS STRUCK BY A POWERFUL WAVE OF COSMIC PARTICLES.

THE SHIELDS CAN'T HOLD! WE'RE GOING DOWN!

MR. FANTASTIC ™

Real Name: Reed Richards
Height: 6' 1"
Weight: 180 lbs
Powers and abilities:
Reed can stretch and contort his body as if it were made of **rubber**. He is also a **scientific genius** with an IQ of over 230.

THE THING ™

Real Name: Ben Grimm
Height: 6'
Weight: 500 lbs
Powers and abilities:
He has a super dense **rocky skin** tough enough to withstand the blast of a surface-to-air missile, plus he's strong enough to lift over **85 tons** without breaking a sweat!

FANTASTIC FOUR ™

4 FANTASTIC FACT!

The Fantastic Four's costumes are made from unstable molecules, allowing them to use their powers without damaging their clothes!

AS THEY CRAWLED FROM THE WRECKAGE, EACH CREW MEMBER WAS SHOCKED TO DISCOVER THE RAYS HAD GIVEN THEM INCREDIBLE POWERS.

SUE STORM COULD TURN INVISIBLE --

REED RICHARDS DISCOVERED HE COULD STRETCH HIS BODY LIKE RUBBER --

JOHNNY WAS ABLE TO CONTROL FIRE --

AND STRANGEST OF ALL, BEN HAD BEEN TRANSFORMED INTO A ROCKY-SKINNED MONSTER!

SWEARING AN OATH TO PROTECT THE WORLD, THEY NOW USE THEIR POWERS TO HELP THOSE IN NEED AS THE *FANTASTIC FOUR!*

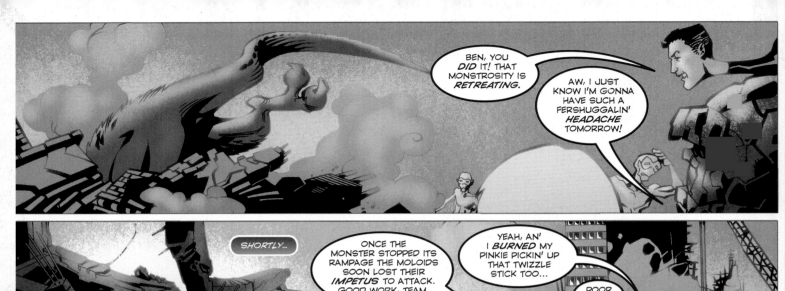

THE END.